Serbin Communications, Inc.

PLAY!

ILLUSTRATION for TOYS and INTERACTIVE GAMES

2006

The 2006 edition of PLAY! Illustration for Toys and Interactive Games is published by Serbin Communications, Inc. in partnership with the Toy Industry Association and the Game Developers Conference

Publisher/Editor	Glen R. Serbin
Vice President/Source Book Director	Elizabeth Nebb Owen
Controller	Radana Khadilkar
Marketing Representatives	Ellie Altomare Jim Christen Jo Ann Miller Beth Pierson
Marketing Assistant	Vicky Kearney
Director of Production	Tamra Dempsey
Production Manager	Barbara Kuhn
Production Staff	Keane Roberts
Distribution Coordinator	Kim Harvey
Proofing	Julie Simpson
Accounting Assistant	Johanna Wagner
Managing Editor/Magazine Division	Julie Simpson
Manager/SiteDesignWorks Division	Christina Henson
Administrative Support	Kim Taylor
Computer Database Coordinator	Debbie Mahterian
Accounting Firm	Damitz, Brooks, Nightingale, Turner & Morrisset
Printer	Toppan Printing Company, LTD.
Shipping & Mailing	Express Logistics, Inc.
Book Design	Design Force, Inc.

www.playillustration.com

A Letter from the Publisher

It is with great pleasure that we present the first annual edition of PLAY! Illustration for Toys and Interactive Games. This project has been in creative development for over two years. After careful research and close consultation with the key players in the toy and interactive game industry, it became clear that there was a specific and growing need for a current, professional resource dedicated to this market.

Serbin Communications has been connecting artists with their markets for over 27 years. For the PLAY! project we combined forces with the Toy Industry Association (TIA) and the Game Developers Conference (GDC) to help us realize our vision of a publication and website highlighting the industry's best artists. Because our partners at TIA and the GDC have a long and central role in their respective markets, they are uniquely positioned to support PLAY!

> "Our goal is for PLAY! to become the primary resource for creative illustration in the Toy and Interactive Game markets."

The increasing need for illustration in both the toy and interactive game markets is global in scope. PLAY! is being sent to hundreds of companies around the world that are looking for the best artists to provide fresh and creative solutions to their projects, no matter where they live.

Creative departments involved in the toy and interactive game markets can now use PLAY! and the companion website www.playillustration.com to hire experienced 2D and 3D image makers. The illustrators presented here can support all phases of product and packaging artwork, from concept and character development to storyboards and comps to finished illustration and animation.

There are many people to thank for their assistance with this project. I first need to thank Elizabeth Owen, our Vice President at Serbin Communications. Elizabeth did an incredible job of helping to build this project from day one. I could not have had a better partner—thanks, Elizabeth! Our marketing staff of Ellie Altomare, Beth Pierson, Jo Ann Miller, Vicky Kearney and Jim Christen did a great job communicating PLAY! to artists.

Special appreciation goes out to Ted Mininni at Design Force. Ted and his team shaped the entire look and feel of PLAY!, including the development of the project name and logo. I am also very fortunate to have a highly professional production staff at our company that I can rely on for all of our internal art production. My appreciation goes to Barbara Kuhn, Tamra Dempsey, and Keane Roberts for all their help in keeping this project on schedule and looking great. A special "thank you" goes to our industry partners, Michele McGuire, Director of Business Strategy at CMP Game Group and Tom Conley, President of the Toy Industry Association for their advice and cooperation.

Our goal is for PLAY! to become the primary resource for creative illustration in the Toy and Interactive Game Markets. Please feel free to write me at glen@serbin.com and let me know your thoughts on PLAY!

Glen R. Serbin

Publisher

Artist and Representatives

Artist and Representatives

5

DOLLS
BICYCLES
ARTS & CRAFTS
BUILDING TOYS
GAMES
BLOCKS
AND MORE...

IT'S PLAYTIME!

Toy Industry Association, Inc. is proud to partner with Serbin Communications to produce PLAY! highlighting the work of the industry's best illustrators and storyboard artists.

Toy Industry Association, Inc.

www.toy-tia.org

3D/Modeling/Animation

Rhythm & Hues/Bernstein & Andriulli

Doug Chezem

11

13

PETER BOLLINGER

14

CLIFF NIELSEN

DAVE SEELEY

CLIFF NIELSEN

DAVE SEELEY

15

Marcel Laverdet

Candy Lab

Studio Liddell

Studio Liddell

Studio Liddell

Studio Liddell

Image Arc

17

AA REPS

American Artists Reps, Inc.
353 West 53rd Street - Suite 1W
New York, NY 10019
Phone: 212.682.2462
Fax: 212.582.0090
Email: info@aareps.com

Find Your Solution
www.aareps.com

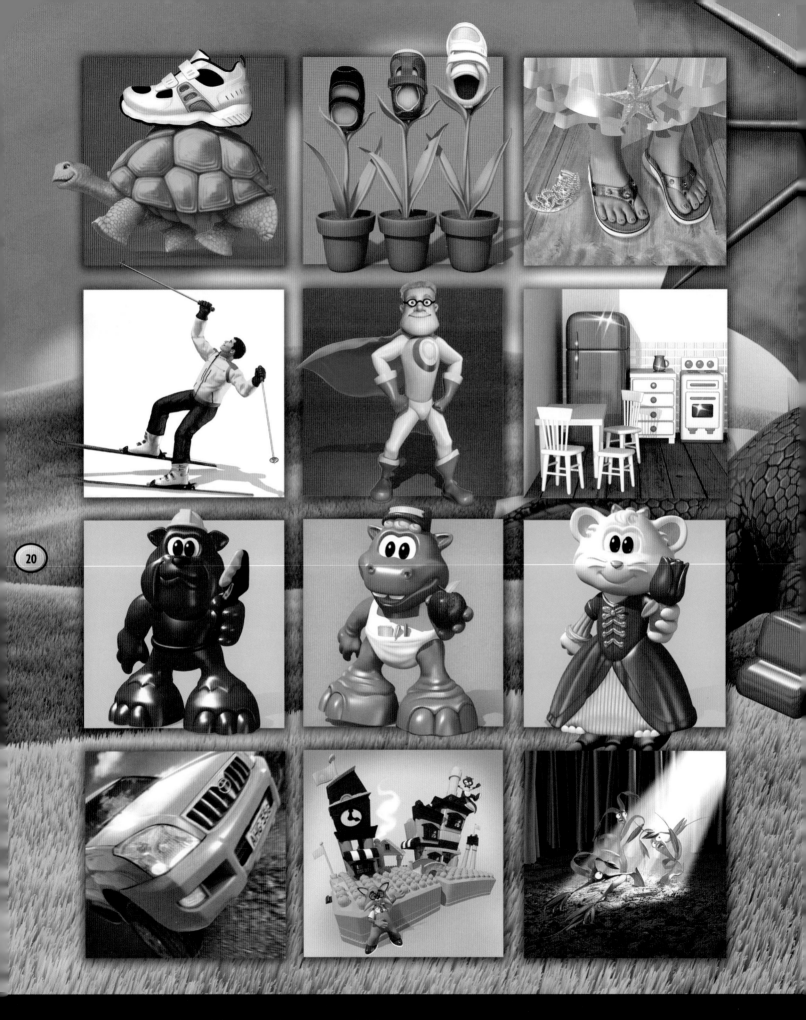

Kim and James

21

Kim and James

KILLER PRICES!

FOR TOP QUALITY ALL-3D DIGITAL ANIMATION, ANIMATICS AND ILLUSTRATION, WE'LL TAKE ON THE FAR EAST, ASIA AND EASTERN EUROPE AND CRUSH THEM ALL. CALL US. WE'LL PROVE IT.

www.wayart.com   101 Fifth Avenue Suite #10E, New York, NY 10003 (212) 604 9957

22

23

TSI Animatics

WAY ART REPRESENTS

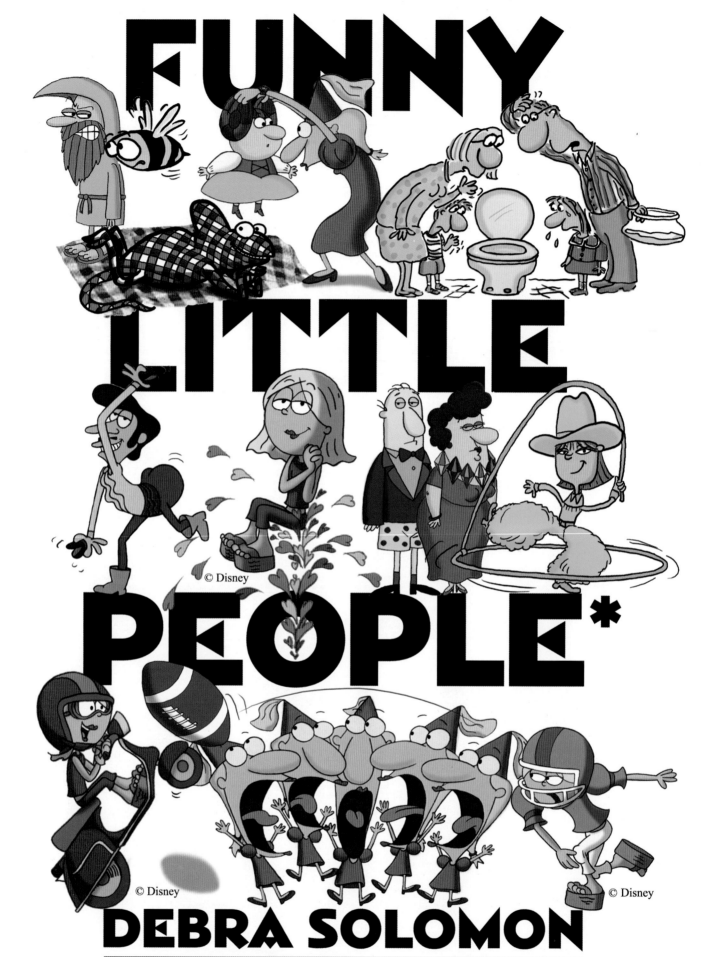

FUNNY LITTLE PEOPLE*

© Disney

© Disney   © Disney

DEBRA SOLOMON

TELEPHONE: 212-619-7900 • CELL: 917-399-7774

CREATOR OF ANIMATED LIZZIE MCGUIRE FOR DISNEY CHANNEL
CLIENTS INCLUDE: AMERICAN EXPRESS • DISNEY CHANNEL • CARTOON
NETWORK • EUROCINEMA CORP. • HBO • HYPERION BOOKS • MCDONALDS • MTV •
NICKELODEON • STAN ROGOW PRODUCTIONS • DEL RIVERO MESSIANU DDB

24

*READY

© Disney

②⑤

TO PLAY

DEBRA SOLOMON

TELEPHONE: 212-619-7900 • CELL: 917-399-7774

CHARACTER DESIGN • DIRECTION AND PRODUCTION
FOR FEATURE FILMS, TELEVISION AND GAMES

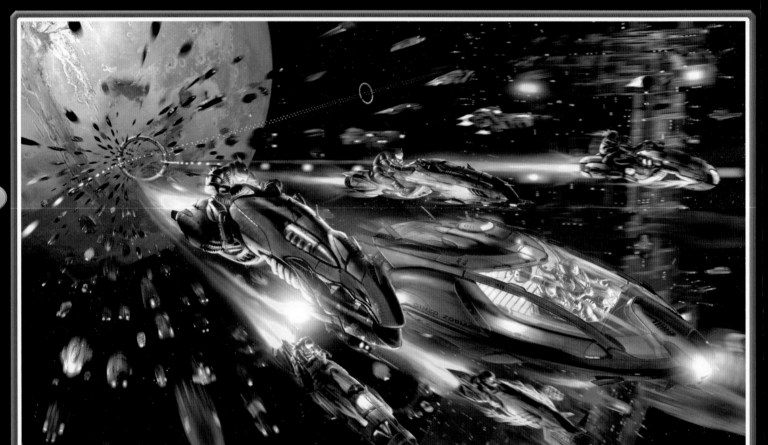

ANIMATION

CHARACTER DEVELOPMENT

CONCEPT DEVELOPMENT

GAME DEVELOPMENT

MATTE PAINTING

STORYBOARDS

WEB GAMING

R+H

D E S I G N

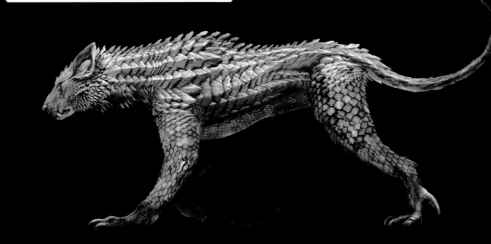

27

BERNSTEIN & ANDRIULLI

www.ba-reps.com

p. 212 682-1490 | f. 212 286-1890 | e. artinfo@ba-reps.com

Rhythm & Hues is represented by Bernstein & Andriulli.

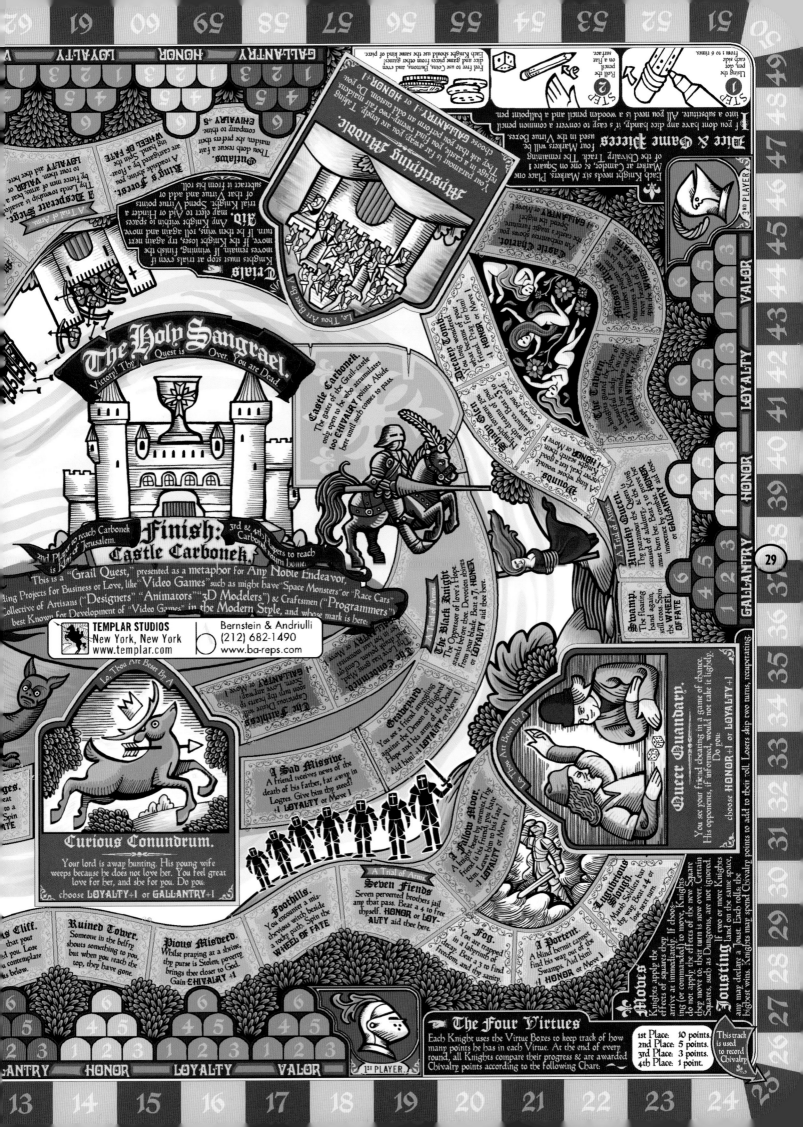

epicstudios
www.epicstudios.com

ILLUSTRATION   ANIMATION

30

33

WAYNE GEORGE SMITH

COLOUR ME LTD

22 HUNTINGDON ROAD, COVENTRY,
WEST MIDLANDS, CV5 6PU, UNITED KINGDOM

SLOWBOY@LOOSE.PLUS.COM

(02476) 672307   WWW.LOOSE.PLUS.COM
                    WWW.COLOUR-ME.CO.UK

Choose C4 for your CGI projects

C4 Digital Entertainment provides high-end computer graphics and digital effects. C4 Digital is a full production studio providing cost effective solutions to your digital needs. Whether it is a pre- rendered television commercial or complete graphical coverage for latest games, C4 has the production capabilities to handle all Computer Generated Imaging.

Digimon property of Bandai America

c4 digital entertainment

www.littlefighteronline.com

C4 handles all forms of CGI:

- COMPUTER ANIMATION
- CHARACTER DESIGN
- 3D MODELING
- INTERFACE DESIGN
- DIGITAL IMAGE PRODUCTION
- DIGITAL EFFECTS
- WEB DESIGN

Best Computer/TV Entertainment Software...Little Fighter Online by U1 Technology Over 3 million users, around the world, who have logged on and played the game. C4 designed over 40 characters for the game.
http://www.hkpc.org/hkdeea/professional_category/little_fighter_online_eng.htm

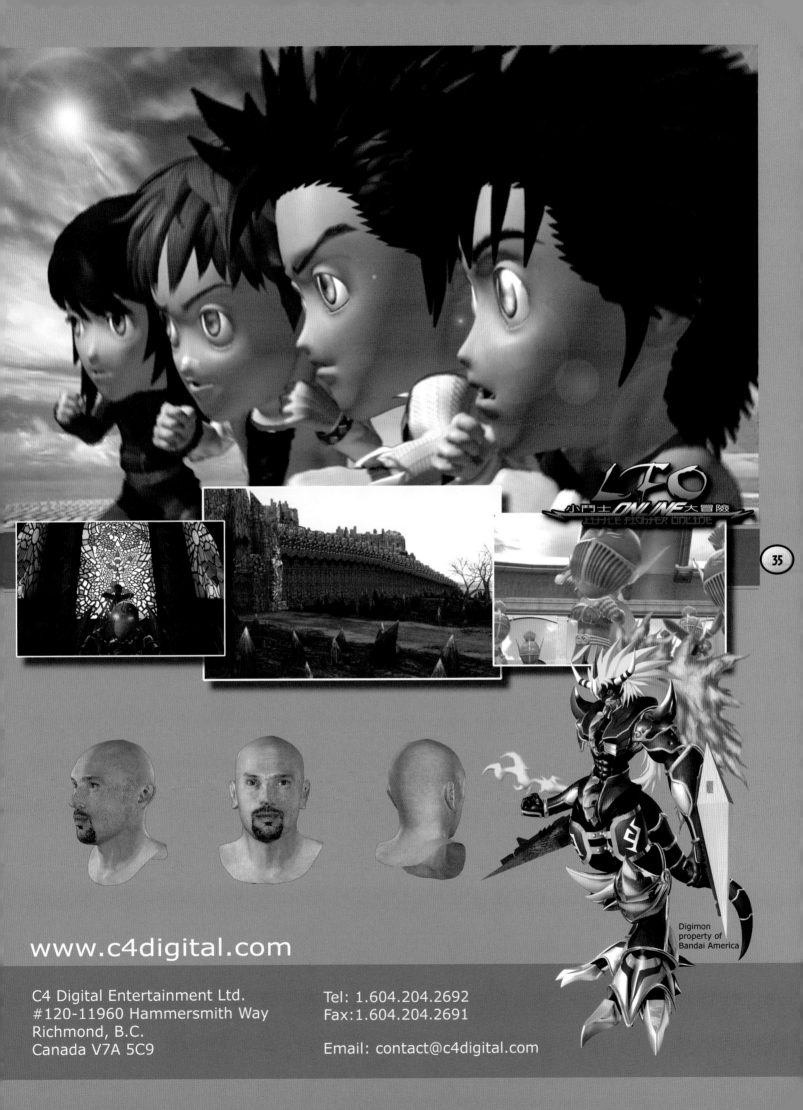

35

www.c4digital.com

C4 Digital Entertainment Ltd.
#120-11960 Hammersmith Way
Richmond, B.C.
Canada V7A 5C9

Tel: 1.604.204.2692
Fax:1.604.204.2691

Email: contact@c4digital.com

Digimon property of Bandai America

DIGITAL ENGINE
STUDIOS

Before

After

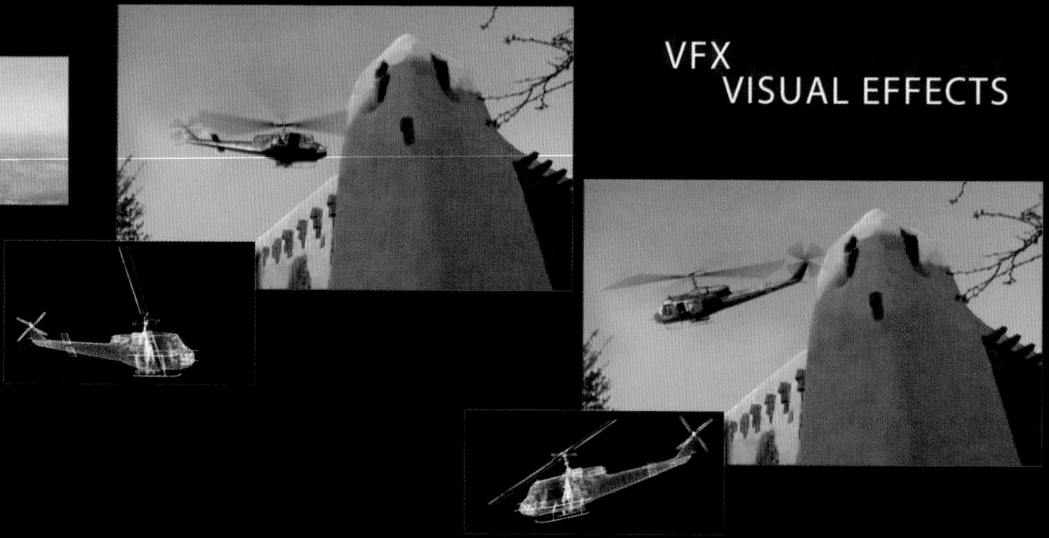

VFX
VISUAL EFFECTS

info@digitalenginestudios.com

512.401.0100

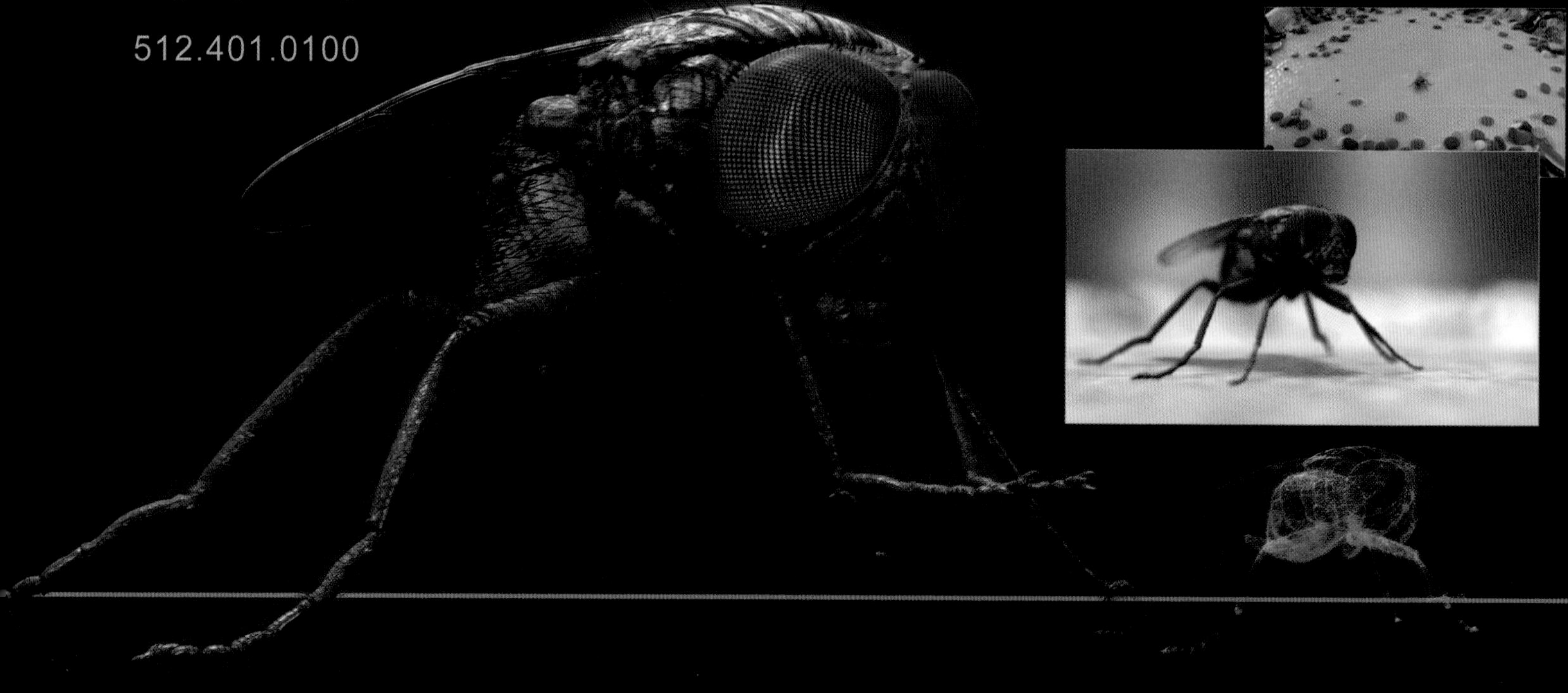

- ## 3D Animation
- ## Motion Graphics
- ## Visual Effects
- ## DVD Production

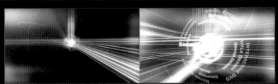
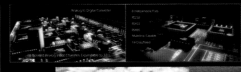

CINEMATIC VISUALS

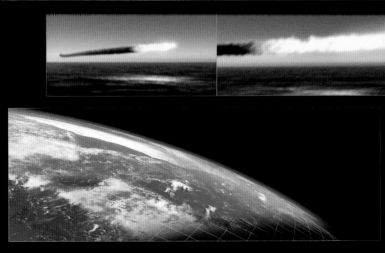

DIGITAL ENVIRONMENTS

www.DigitalEngineStudios.com

MOTION ARTISTS AGENCY

www.motionartists.com   motionartists@sbcglobal.net   323-663-6349

STORYBOARDS / 2D - 3D CONCEPTUAL ART

BENEFITS
DISCOUNTS
EVENTS
MARKETING
MEMBERSHIP
SAFETY
CREDIT
PROMOTION

(40)

JOIN TIA

AND START REAPING THE BENEFITS
OF MEMBERSHIP TODAY!

For details on membership or TIA's various trade shows and events, visit TIA's website at **www.toy-tia.org** or contact us at info@toy-tia.org; phone: 212-675-1141.

Toy Industry Association, Inc.™ (TIA) is recognized by government, the trade, media and consumers as the authoritative voice of the North American toy industry.

Toy Industry Association, Inc.

www.toy-tia.org

41

Shawn Murphy

Espinosa

wiKid
brand©

42

Otis+
Rae©

sushi
pack
sushi
pack
ワサビ

wasabi

Espinosa

kiko™
macaco

STUDIO ESPINOSA
P 1+617 441 7773 F 1+617 945 0187
11 WRIGHT STREET #1 CAMBRIDGE, MA 02138 USA

WWW.STUDIOESPINOSA.COM

43

How to make a MASK...

HERE'S WHAT YOU NEED:

scissors

GLOO
FOR STICKING -
NOT LICKING!

like it says

some candy corn

a paper bag

Step One →

Cut out Some fancy Shapes

cut
cut
cut

STEP TWO →

Eat most of the Candy Corn. Glue the FANCY SHAPES to YOUR FACE!

NEATO!

©nyj

When's the last time you got to work with an illustrator who started out as a clown?

HAPPY SUMMER

HAPPY SUMMER

glue

Magic beans

NYJ

KEEP YER MITTS PINCHERS TO YERSELF!

Nathan Y. Jarvis 801-831-0406

44

www.nathanjarvis.com

Making people stop, smile, read, think, laugh, learn and/or buy stuff for more than 217 dog years.

Nathan Y. Jarvis   801-831-0406

nathan@nathanjarvis.com

CONTACT

45

mow

boef

NYJ

Kid-Friendly Stuff

© MATTEL

Accessories

46

mona daly

contact   www.dasgrup.com

carrie perlow: p: 310.540.5958   east: mendola artists   p: 212.986.5680

www.dasgrup.com

47

©MATTEL

48

© MATTEL

ray goudey

contact   www.dasgrup.com

carrie perlow: p: 310.540.5958

© MATTEL

www.dasgrup.com

49

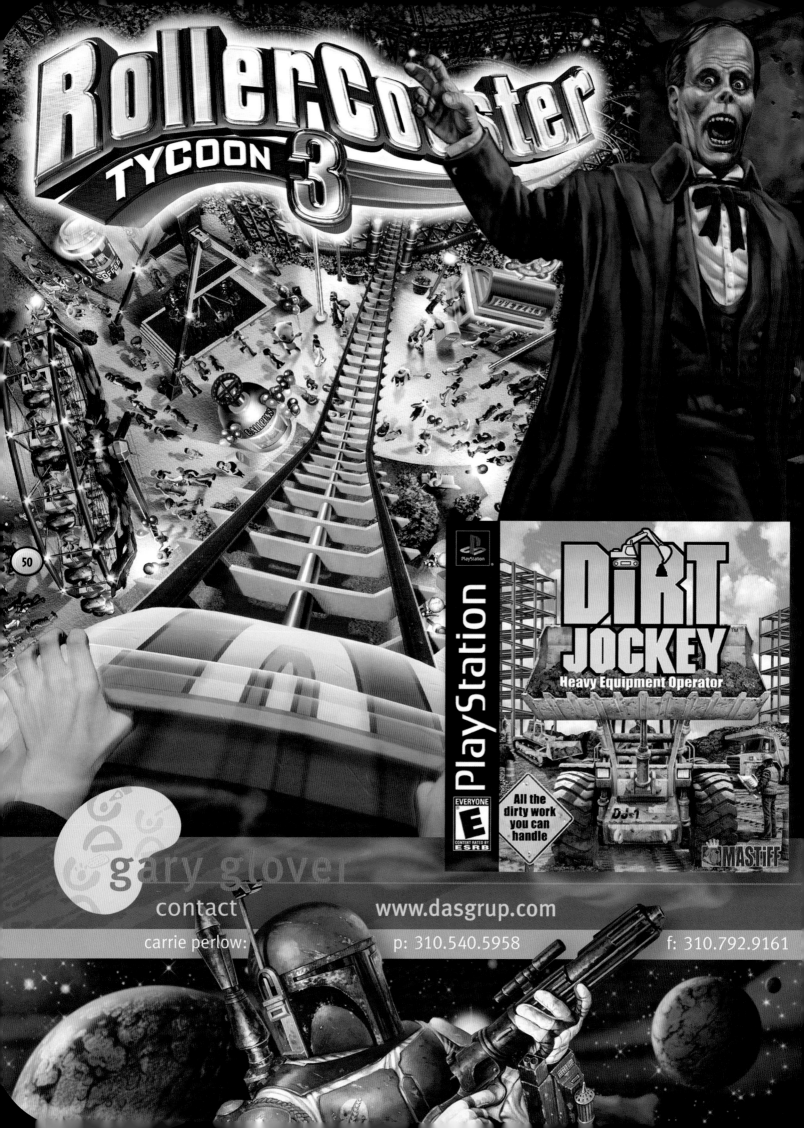

Toy Design

Illustration

Packaging

Characters

52

Marketing
Materials

Coloring Books
& Activities

Cartoons

Logos

MISSY
MONKEY DOODLE

4 working
hands!

Get a gander at our portfolios
www.monkeydoodledandy.com

Kurt's email
Kurt@monkeydoodledandy.com

Elaine's email
Elaine@monkeydoodledandy.com

718.398.2338
Monkey Doodle Dandy, Inc 219 17th Street, Suite 3B, Brooklyn, NY 11215

BILL MAYER WWW.THEBILLMAYER.COM 404-378-0686

REPRESENTED BY TRICIA WEBER 212-799-6532

55

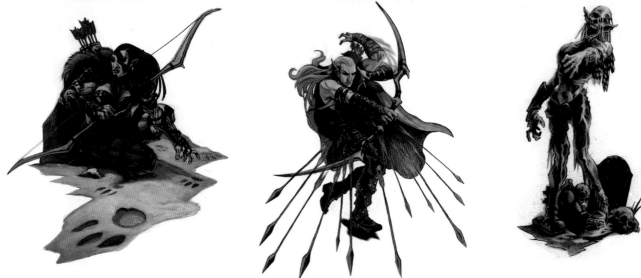

Concept • Design • Illustration

Steve Ellis

WWW.HYPERACTIVEART.COM

STEVE@HYPERACTIVEART.COM

Clients Include:
Hasbro • Wizards of the Coast • Marvel Enterprises
• Taratoy • Whitewolf Publishing • Alderac Entertainment Group
• Scholastic Books • DC Comics • Sabertooth Games...

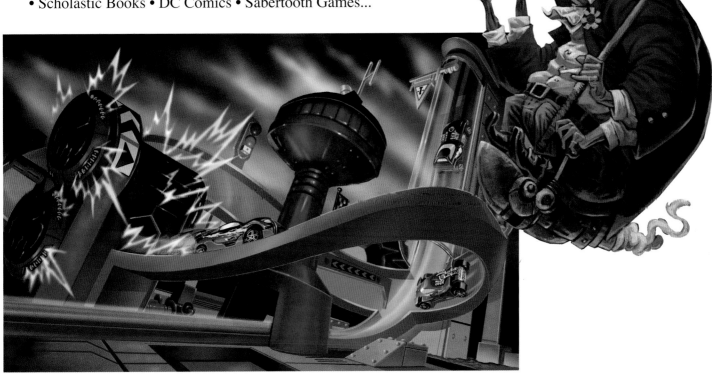

Todd Mueller
Illustration & Design
email: todd@toddmueller.net
www.toddmueller.net
Ph/Fax: 303-367-5970

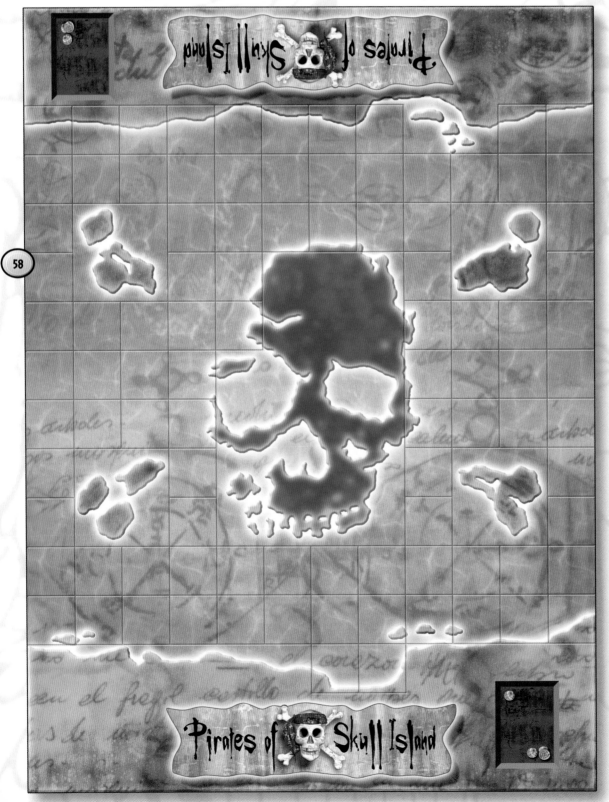

Pirates of Skull Island

STANGORMAN

310 265.7434
info@stangorman.com
www.stangorman.com

S. GORMAN

60

Video game concept, Williams Entertainment.

STAN GORMAN

310 265.7434
info@stangorman.com
www.stangorman.com

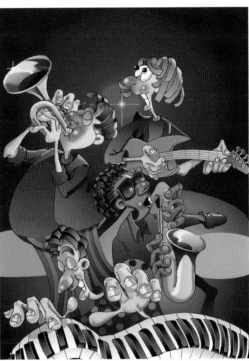

Hanes Underware

IsopThor pest control magazine ad, and Flash animation.

SKAGGS DESIGN

314-631-5363

craigskaggs@sbcglobal.net

SpongeBob SquarePants

62

63

67

www.daryllcollins.com

Daryll Collins / 513.683-9335

KENNY FULLER

Illustration, Character & Concept Art

©Kenny Fuller 2005

www.fullerillustration.com

TRACE
WWW.TRACYCOX.COM
415.336.4379
TRACESTER@GMAIL.COM
ILLUSTRATION

71

72

mike dammer

312.782.4995
www.mikedammer.com

robert zimmerman studio

interactive

www.zimm.net
828.252.4773

◀ detail from
The Great Bug Off

try it out at Discovery.com
kids.discovery.com/games/bugoff/bugoff.html

• all animation, flash programming, sound
track, game design and concept done
in-house.

Chomp and Temple of Puzzles

play it at Discovery.com
kids.discovery.com/games/chomp/chomp.html

• animation, flash programming, sound
track, game design and concept by us

at last count, being played
SIX HUNDRED THOUSAND
times EVERY DAY!

◀ detail from
The Mad Monkey Math Vault

About the interactive game thing:

You can see more interactive game stuff and link to the above games at the web site, **zimm.net**.
If flash games are something you'd like to talk about for your, or your clients web site, give
the studio a call. We create custom online presentations for all games, and will even travel
to you to do a song and dance about game ideas.

& stuff

robert zimmerman studio
www.zimm.net
828.252.4773

Five color pen thing
for Klutz Press

Promotional packaging
for General Mills

Little bouncy balls
from Crocodile Creek

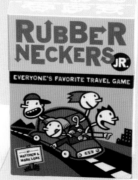

Rubber Neckers and
Rubber Neckers, Jr.
From Chronicle Books

CRITTEROLOGY™ jungle

651.436.8855 • redracerstudio.com

651.436.8855 • redracerstudio.com

77

RED RACER STUDIO • ILLUSTRATION • PACKAGE & GRAPHIC DESIGN • TOY DEVELOPMENT

Monte Michael Moore
Maverick Illustration
Client List: Lucasfilm Ltd, Playboy
Coors, Microsoft, Playstation2, DC
Comics, Marvel Comics, StarTrek.

5360 N. Franklin St.
Denver, CO 80216
303-294-0146

mavmktg@Qadas.com
www.mavarts.com
www.myndzei.com

78

Realistic
Whimsical
Black & White
Packaging Art
Dynamic
Sexy
Bold

PlayStation 2
X-TREME
QUADS

3+

LEGION
ONLY THE STRONG SURVIVE

Concept Art
Toy Design
Cover Art   79
Character Design
Sculpture Design

Games

SHAUN A

All Characters and designs
this page © Copyright Monte Moore

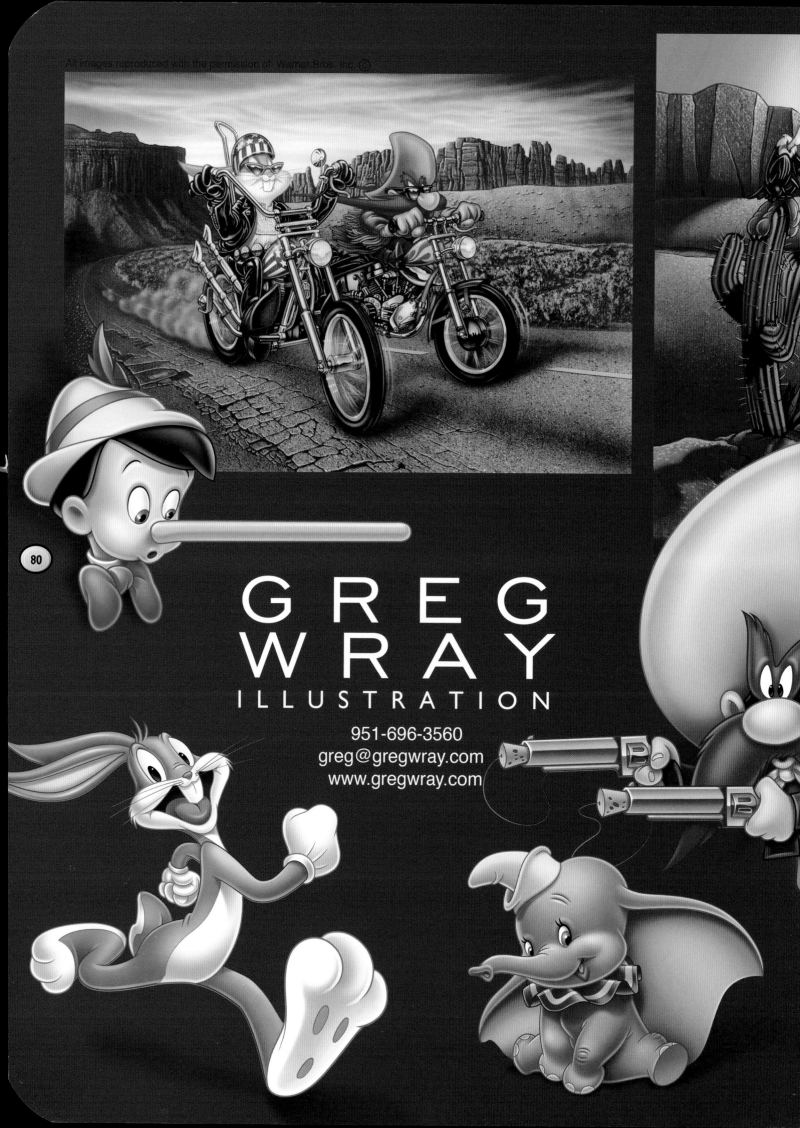

80

GREG WRAY

ILLUSTRATION

951-696-3560
greg@gregwray.com
www.gregwray.com

DaVe
CLeGG

p77o.887.63o6
f77o.781.578o
www.cleggo.com
dave@cleggo.com

82

Charlene Maguire

www.shapeshifterstudios.net
charlene@shapeshifterstudios.net :: 310.927.7154

MICHAEL GRAHAM
ILLUSTRATOR

336-778-0932 • mike@michaelgraham-art.com
4530 Greenfield Way Drive • Winston-Salem • NC • 27103

Blueberry   Vladimir   Barnabus   Khan

Zone KiDS

The Journey
Begins!

Peeper

Cleo Thistledown
Forest Sprite

Story by:
Peter Parente

The Kinkajou

19 Bowers Ave. Tyngsboro, MA 01879   978-957-1324   www.amosink.com

Jeff Easley
Illustration & Conceptual Design
262-248-0230   Email: caraeas@yahoo.com   www.jeffeasley.com

91

Imagine

Alan F. Beck

Artist • Illustrator
Brooklyn, NY

www.alanfbeck.com
alanfbeck@earthlink.net
Phone: 347-495-8138

Science Fiction • Fantasy • Surrealism • 3-D Modeling
Traditional and digital media

95

Bill Hall • www.billhall.com • 972-299-5102

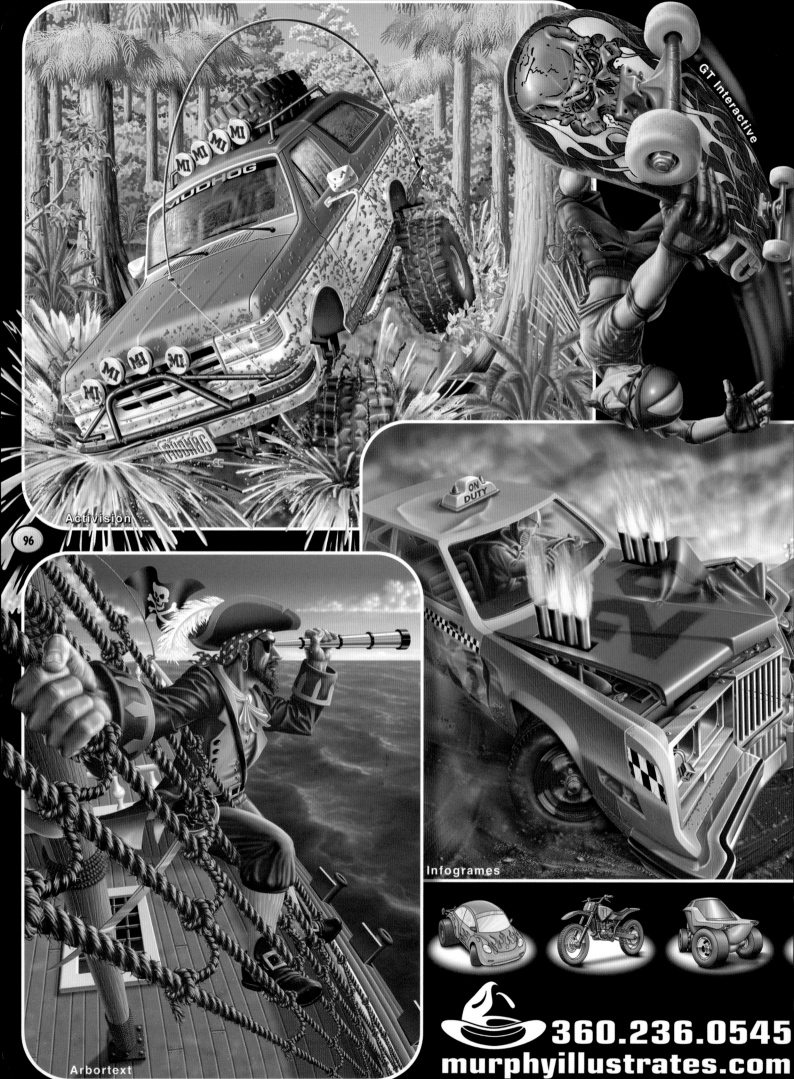

Activision

96

GT Interactive

Infogrames

Arbortext

Wallsdecor

97

Radica Games

COUNTY FAIR

Mattel

98

CHARACTER DESIGN & ILLUSTRATION: YOUTH, RPG, MASCOTS • LOGO

EMacDESIGN.com
Eric@EMacDESIGN.com
703.834.0030

COVER ART • BOOK ILLUSTRATION • STORYBOARDS

Award-winning design

20 years experience

Complete in-house services

Inno

Point-of-sale

Friendly service

branding solutions

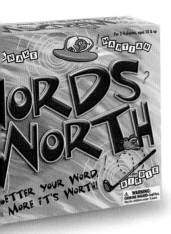

Serving clients large & small

101

ZELEZNIK ILLUSTRATION

PACKAGING • CONCEPT • CHARACTER DESIGN

661-799-9987

WWW.JOHNZELEZNIK.COM

102

The Art of
BOBBY CHIU

Freelance Artist
www.ARTOFBOB.COM

The Art of
BOBBY CHIU

www.artofbob.com

ADRIAN JOHNSON

BENJAMIN WACHENJE

CHRIS MOORE

DAVE NEEDHAM

GARY BASEMAN

JONAS BERGSTRAND

JON BURGERMAN

KRISTIAN OLSON

LEE MACLEOD

MAX ELLIS

MICK MARSTON

PAM WALL

SHINICHI SHIRASHI

107

BERNSTEIN & ANDRIULLI

www.ba-reps.com

p. 212 682-1490 | f. 212 286-1890 | e. artinfo@ba-reps.com

108

©2006 Bernstein & Andriulli Inc.

ADAM WILLIS

BOB LEA

LARRY ROSTANT

MARTYN PICK

MEL GRANT

PAUL YOUNG

SAM HADLEY

STEPHEN PLAYER

STEVE STONE

illustration I graphics I creative & brand consultancy I interactive I game development
web design I characters I animated encounters I 3D renderings I storyboards I exhibitions
paintings I toys I robots I merchandise

BERNSTEIN & ANDRIULLI

www.ba-reps.com

p. 212 682-1490 | f. 212 286-1890 | e. artinfo@ba-reps.com

Artist Partners is represented by Bernstein & Andriulli in the United States.

THUNDERDOG
BRAINSTORMING A CLOUDED WORLD

Hey you! Do you need some art? How about a toy? Just cut & paste! It's that easy!

4"

BIG POPPA

d e d

110

TOY DESIGN ①
TOY PRODUCTION ②
ILLUSTRATION ③
CHARACTER DESIGN ④
BRANDING & LOGO DESIGN ⑤

Spike Video Game AWARDS 2004

Filith

kid robot

Cut along the dotted line!

111

THUNDER DOG

BERNSTEIN & ANDRIULLI
p. 212 682-1490 | f. 212 286-1890 | e. artinfo@ba-reps.com
www.ba-reps.com

Thunderdog is represented by Bernstein & Andriulli
©2006 Bernstein & Andriulli Inc.

WWW.ALANPOLLACK.COM

113

twi

RADIO CONTROL CAR ACTION
20TH
ANNIVERSARY
1985 · 2005

Trivial Pursuit
DVD
Pop Culture
GAME

Trivial Pursuit
DVD
Pop Culture
GAME

BATTLE BALL GAME
ULTIMATE
SCORE
SWEEPSTAKES

ULTIMATE
NFL
NFL

twi · visual and typographic solutions at play · 212.866.8166 · tom@tw-eye.com · www.tw-eye.com

ericjoyner.com
415.974.0708 Studio – 415.305.3992 Cell
eric@ericjoyner.com

CYBÉLE

JASON EDMISTON

MATTHIEU ROUSSEL

TYRONE MᶜCARTHY

121

Chris Boyd
Character Design and Illustration
www.crazy3dman.com
708-369-9802

123

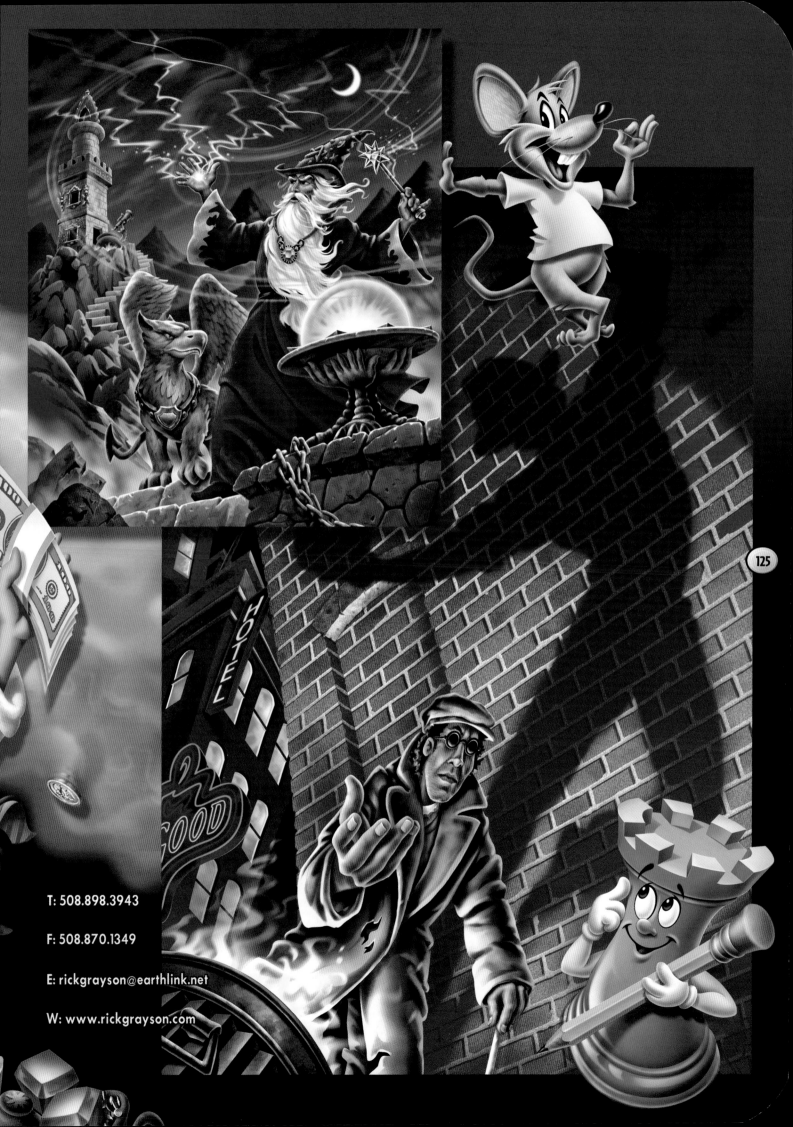

T: 508.898.3943

F: 508.870.1349

E: rickgrayson@earthlink.net

W: www.rickgrayson.com

125

126

Represented by **Patricia Goudreau** 413.967.9855 pgreps.com

Gary LaCoste

Roc Goudreau
Illustrator / Designer

129

Character Designs

Visual Development

Storyboards

Eddie Pittman
Character Designs

131

KIRK MANLEY

ILLUSTRATION   CHARACTER DESIGN   CONCEPT
888 · 211 · 6864   203 · 255 · 7541

132

MANLEY 04

D e n n i s   A l l a i n

Architecture Design Illustration

50 fairview road
lynnfield, massachusetts
01940

Phone: 781 5 9 2 9 2 8 4

www.dennisallain.com
dennis@dennisallain.com

134

Project: Observatorium
Client: self promotional

Project: Wackasau Fairgrounds
Client: self promotional

Project: Coda 2002
Client: self promotional

Project: 'Toy Store'
Client: Hasbro

Project: (withheld)
Client: Disney

Project: Bluebeards Demise
Client: self promotional

1 2

3

dennis allain has been designing and illustrating for nearly 20 years. His design studio has dedicated itself to creating highly evocative imagery that captivates the imagination and invigorates the spirit.

dennis has provided design and illustrative content to such firms as: Hasbro, Disney, AT&T Lego, McDonalds, and Martyr Press Comics.

'what is possible in art becomes thinkable in life'

Brian Eno

v
a
r
i
o
u
s

4

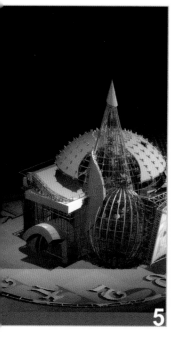

5

6

insert: digital wireframe

135

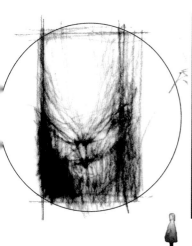

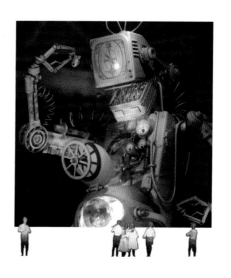

138

139

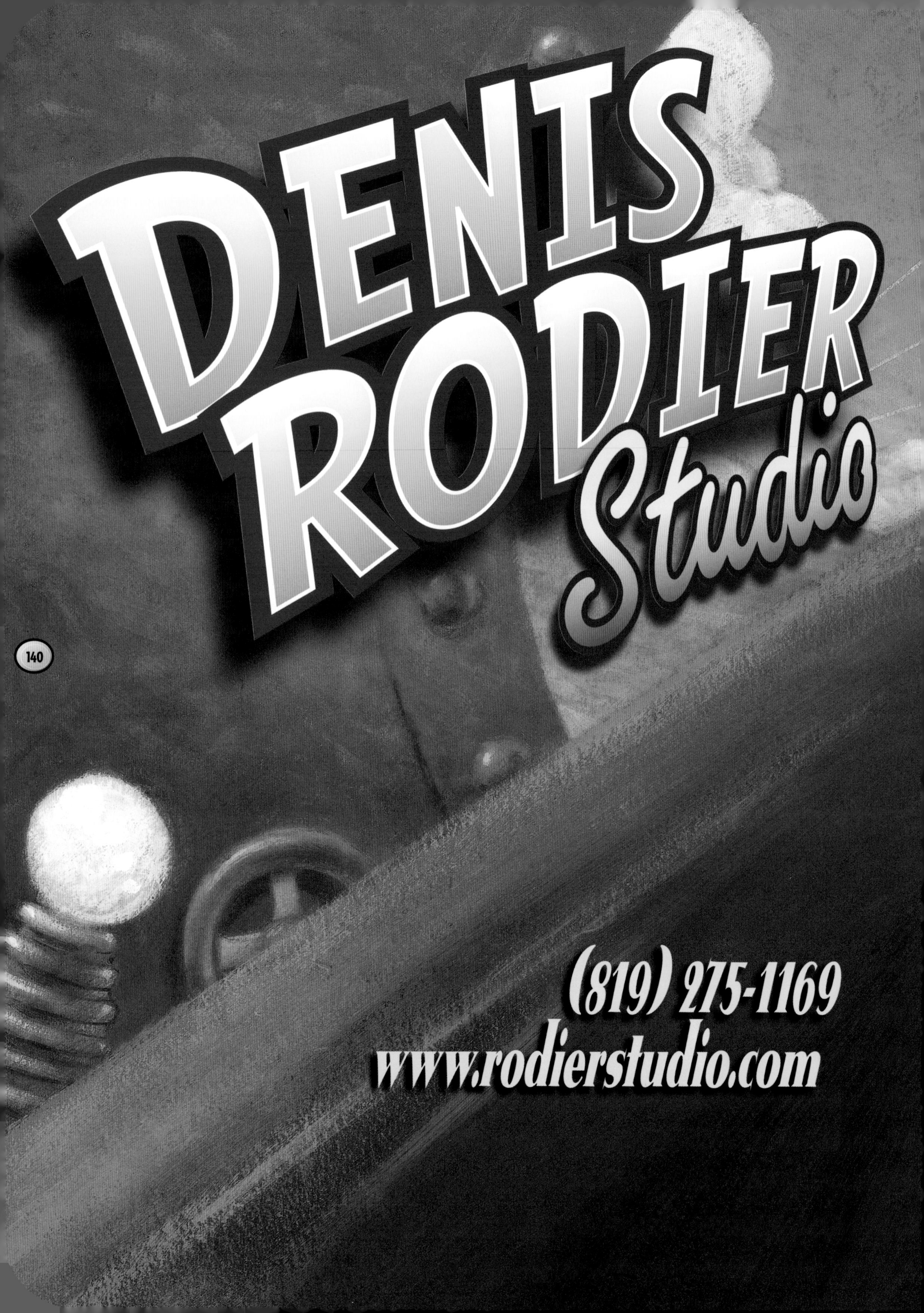

DENIS RODIER *Studio*

140

(819) 275-1169
www.rodierstudio.com

WACK

JEFF WACK ILLUSTRATION

jeffwack.com
818-766-0348
818-508-0348
wackart@pacbell.net

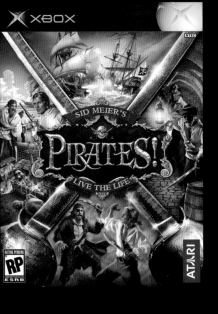

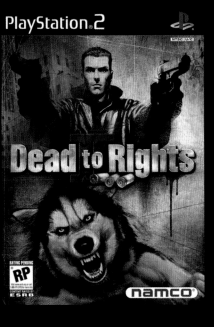

WACK

JEFF WACK ILLUSTRATION

jeffwack.com

818-766-0348

818-508-0348

wackart@pacbell.net

143

144

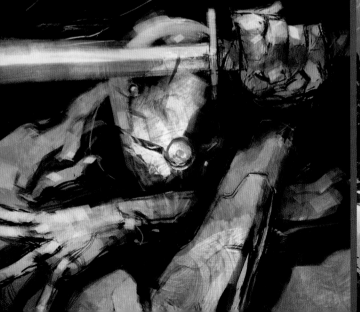

COMIC BOOK STYLE ART!

147

CUSTOM COMICS & ART

SILENT HILL

CVO: COVERT VAMPIRIC OPERATIONS

MARC ERICKSEN ILLUSTRATION

1045   Sansome Street, Studio 306

San Francisco, CA
94111

(415). 362.1214

Galoob Toys
Tyco Toys
Zee Toys
Damert inc.
Marvel Toys
Radio Shack
Electronic Arts
Activision
Dime Store Dreams
Spinmasters
Shoot the Moon
Broderbund
Star Tours
Atari

marc@marcericksen.com

148

URL: marcericksen.com

MARC ERICKSEN ILLUSTRATION

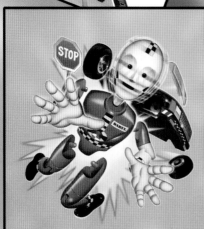

(415).362.1214

marcericksen.com

marc@marcericksen.com

149

GLAM GiRLS

lisa

www.lisahenderling.com 845 876 8736

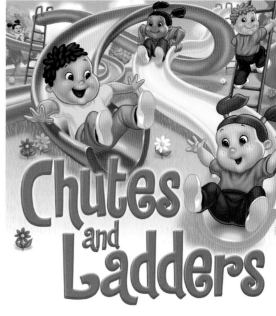

152

153

MENDOLA
ARTISTS REPRESENTATIVES

WWW.MENDOLAART.COM

PH 212.986.5680 | E mendolaart@aol.com

Jim Talbot

Captain Krook

Woody

One-Eyed Pete

McScurvy

Salted Pork

CAPTAIN METROLOGY

154

MAIN MENU

New game
Continue game
Practice
Options
High Scores

Cancel   Save   Play

PRO SHOP

◄ Weapons ►

Semi Automatic Type 2

This is a semi-automatic gun. It has an improved barrel for accuracy and a bottom line kit for improvedrate of fire. A bottom line kit moves the air tank to face backwards instead of forward. It makes firing easier.

Equip   Buy

Cancel   Save   Play

157

Brian Ajhar

Gerald & Cullen Rapp

212 889 3337

www.rappart.com
www.ajhar.com

Character Design & Illustration

160

MARC ROSENTHAL

Gerald & Cullen Rapp • 212.889.3337 • www.rappart.com • www.marc-rosenthal.com

Brian Biggs
www.MrBiggs.com
REPRESENTED by GERALD & CULLEN RAPP
(212) 889-3337 www.RappArt.com

iLLUStRAtiON · CHARACtERS · LEttERiNG · COMiCS
ANiMAtiON (FLaSH, etc) · dESiGN · tRAiNEd MONKEYS

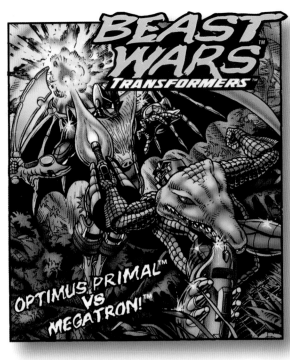

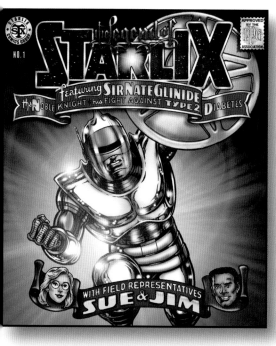

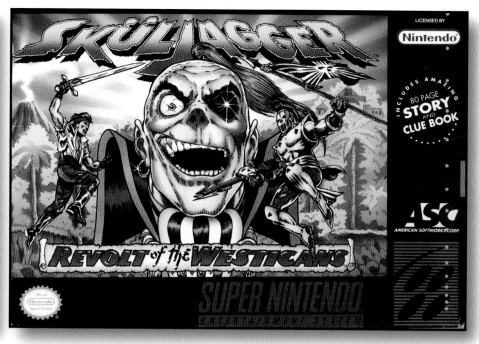

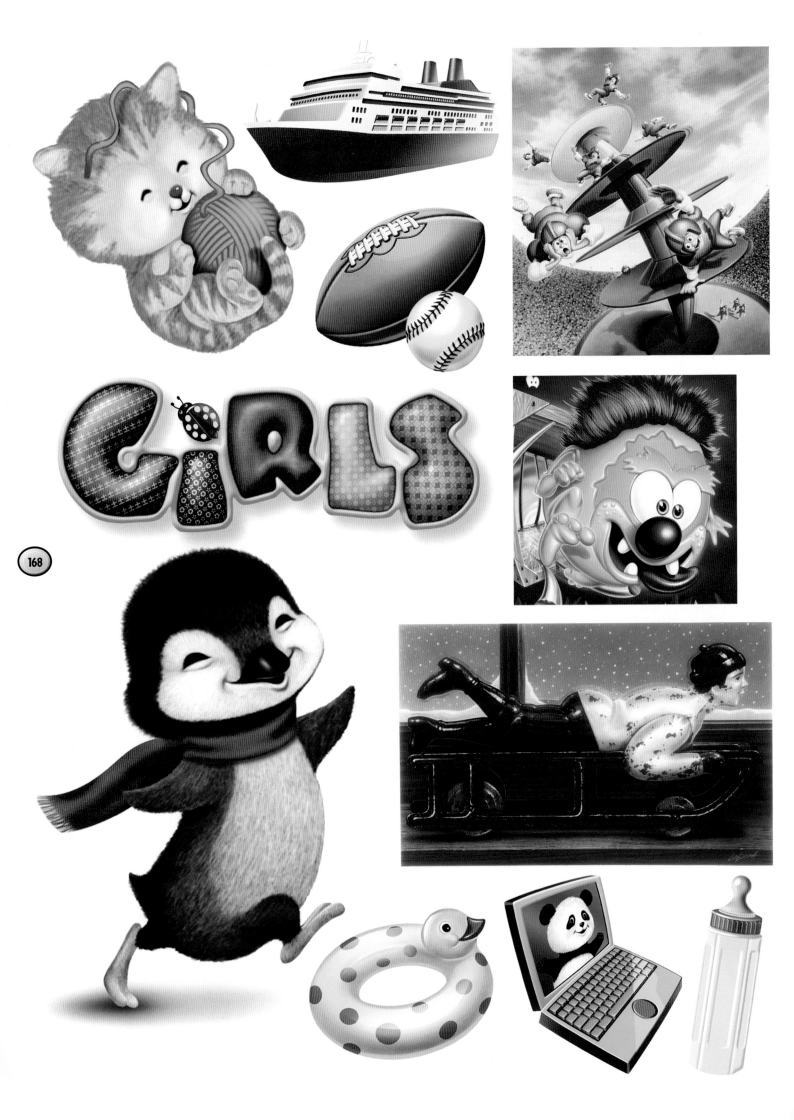

GIRLS

168

LORIOART.COM

Lori Osiecki
123 W. 2nd Street
Mesa AZ 85201
lorioart@mac.com
480-962-5233

170

Schmingdom KINGDOM™

LORIOART.COM

480-962-5233

TELL ME WHAT YOU NEED. I'LL DEVELOP YOUR IDEA INTO A CUTE, VIABLE TOY PRESENTATION!

MATTEL

wendyall.com

WE NEED JUNGLE THEMED NURSERY FURNITURE FOR BABY LION KING.

see more at wendyall.com

WE NEED A DISNEY CASTLE PLAYSET CONSTRUCTED OUT OF FOME CORE FOR A 3-D PRESENTATION.

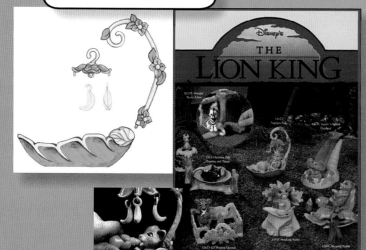

WE NEED A MAGIC COSTUME SHOP THEMED PLAYSET FOR MY LITTLE PONY.

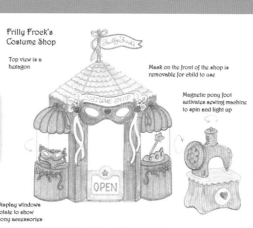

173

WE NEED ILLUSTRATIONS FOR BARBIE AMERICAN STORIES COLLECTOR BOOKS.

WE NEED COSTUME CONCEPTS FOR CABBAGE PATCH KIDS GARDEN FAIRIES.

RAY MARSHALL DESIGN

GRAPHIC DESIGN

2D-3D ILLUSTRATION

PAPER ENGINEERING

510·595·1566

ray@raymarshalldesign.com

To see more work examples
please visit
www.raymarshalldesign.com

176

3D model

*Laser-cut
Holiday card*

*Pop-up magazine
advertisement*

3D illustration
for childrens book

177

© Ray Marshall 2005

3D PIXELS
3D PAPER

Direct mail pop-up

...into outstanding results!

The Circus is Coming...

ORACLE
FESTIVAL of COLORS
Summer Picnic '90

Pop-up event invitation

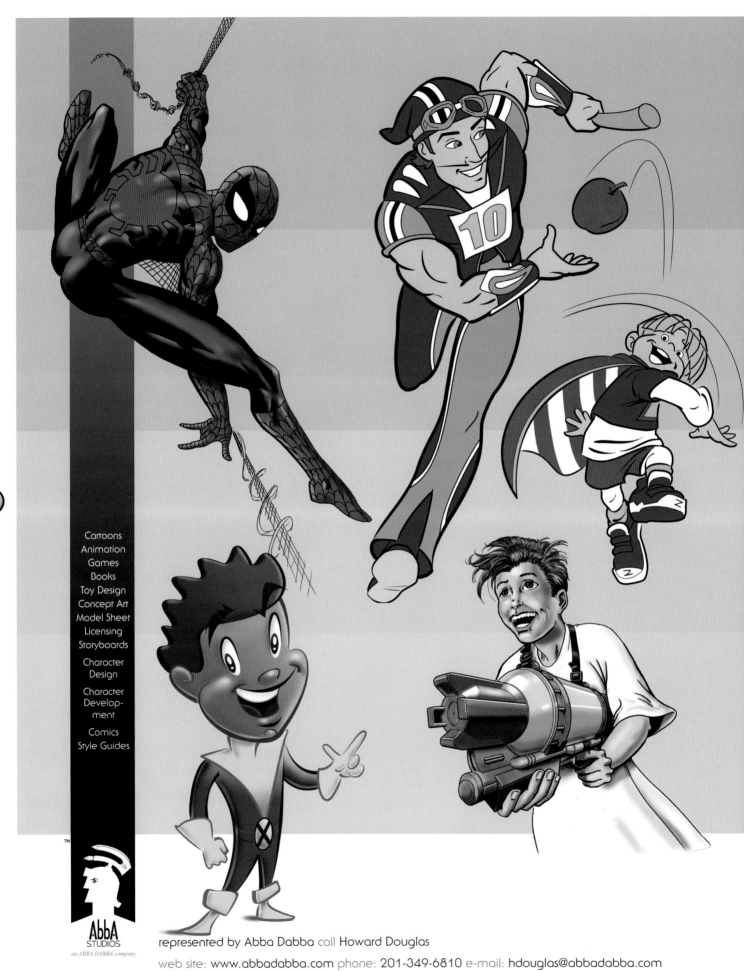

Cartoons
Animation
Games
Books
Toy Design
Concept Art
Model Sheet
Licensing
Storyboards
Character
Design
Character
Develop-
ment
Comics
Style Guides

AbbA
STUDIOS
an ABBA DABBA company

represented by Abba Dabba call Howard Douglas

web site: www.abbadabba.com phone: 201-349-6810 e-mail: hdouglas@abbadabba.com

179

AbbA
STUDIOS

represented by Abba Dabba call Howard Douglas
web site: www.abbadabba.com phone: 201-349-6810 e-mail: hdouglas@abbadabba.com

Michel Bohbot-www.mbohbot.com
510-547-0667 Game, Toy and Book art

Represented by **Donna Cameron**
Tel: 604 684-6826 Fax: 604 733-4422
www.repart.com

Character • Concept • Production • Packaging

183

JOHN BREWSTER

JAMES SILVANI

(203)226-4724

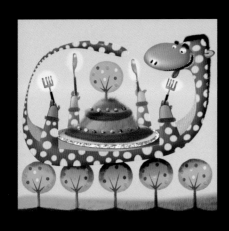
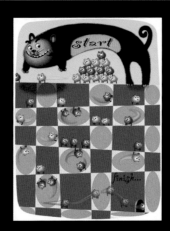

KEN GAMAGE

WWW.BREWSTERCREATIVE.COM

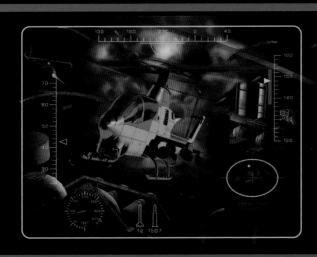
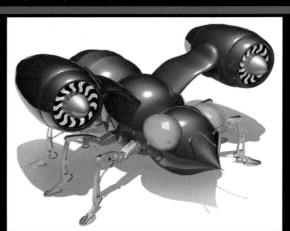

GLENN GUSTAFSON

CREATIVE.SVCS@SNET.NET

184

CREATIVE SERVICES

MARTY BAUMANN

SHAYNE LETANE

185

 (203)226-4724 Fax (203)454-9904

 35 Franklin Street, Westport, CT 06880

 CREATIVE.SVCS@SNET.NET

WWW.BREWSTERCREATIVE.COM

186

TEL : 212 239-4946
Email: artworksillustration@earthlink.net
Web: artworksillustration.com
More images: theispot.com//repartworksillustration

 works   *Jerry Vanderstelt*

vanderstelt studio.com

187

TEL : 212 239-4946
Email: artworksillustration@earthlink.net
Web: artworksillustration.com
More images: theispot.com//repartworksillustration

works   *Jerry Vanderstelt*

188

CHRIS BUTLER

PHONE: (303)530-4695
FAX: (303) 530-5036

For additional samples of more than 200 illustrations, call or fax
your request, or email me at: artzguy1@comcast.net

191

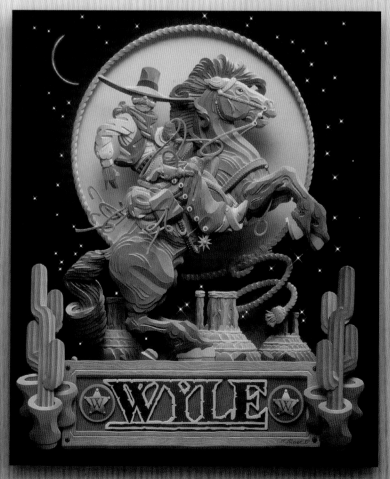

Franken-Frog

Count Frogula

193

Conceptual Illustration

kevin pope

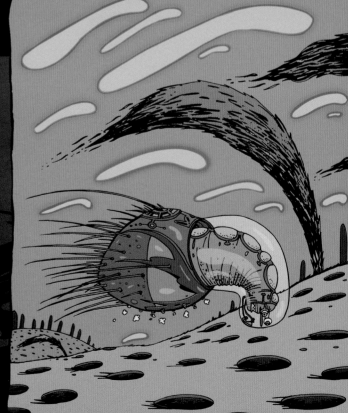

We do it all …

design

writing

illustration

photography

product development

photo manipulation

CONDICT AND COMPANY

ph 610.845.8851

fx 610.845.8858

10 north front street, bally, pa 19503

acondict@condictandco.com

www.condictandco.com

a Goose Finds Christmas

by Darlene Moll Roth
illustrations by Amanda Lee Condict

199

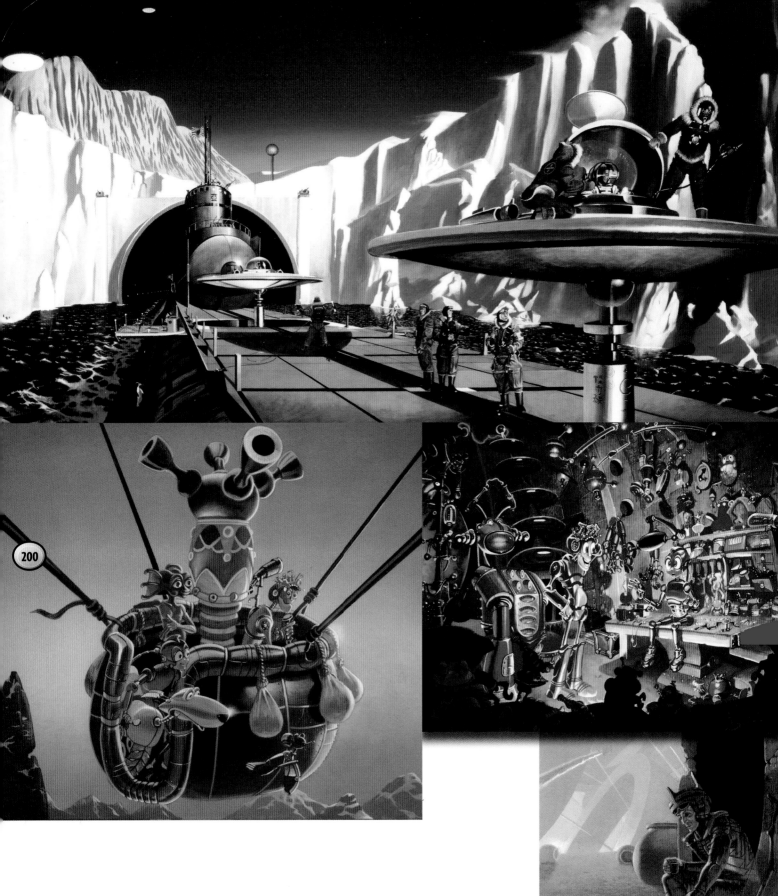

Alan H. Okamoto
ILLUSTRATION

415-626-2501
alanokamoto.com
jinden@earthlink.net
alan_h_okamoto@yahoo.com

Max Goes to the Moon

A Science Adventure with Max the Dog

Jeffrey Bennett

Illustrated by

Alan Okamoto

Max Goes to Mars

A Science Adventure with Max the Dog

Jeffrey Bennett

Illustrated by

Alan Okamoto

Matt Andrews
ILLUSTRATION

OPTIONS

15+ years experience with electronic and printed art

Style suits board or electronic games!

Kid-friendly touch that appeals to adults as well!

Storyboarding and character development as well as art for finished packaging!

www.mattandrews.net
mail@mattandrews.net
(856) 981-6096

203

SLEDD
STUDIOS

JOHN W. SLEDD

800.861.5784

703.349.1336

john@sledd.com

www.sledd.com

Jason Farris

Digital Illustration   Packaging Design   Graphic Design   Concept Art   www.jasonfarris.com   815-520-7573

FamousFrames

Toy & Video Game Packaging
Storyboards, Cinematics
Concept & Design...

RISE of NATIONS

Halo I, II - Twisted Metal - Blade II - Tron II - Dune - Serious Sam
Lord Of The Rings - Command and Conquer... and more...

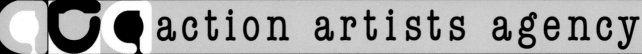
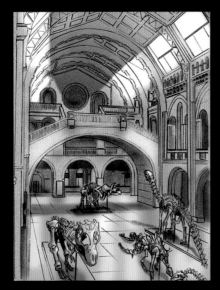

JEFF NENTRUP DESIGN

JEFF NENTRUP DESIGN

CARLOS VERA
CHRISTIAN HOPE
JEFF NENTRUP
JIM BANDSUH
VINCENT LUCIDO

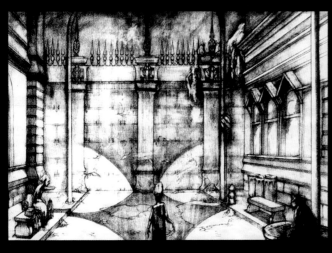

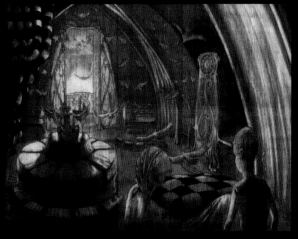

212

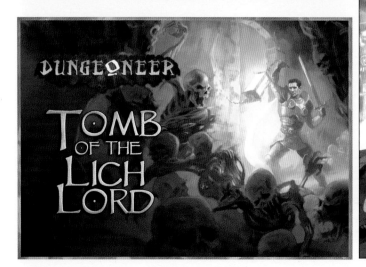

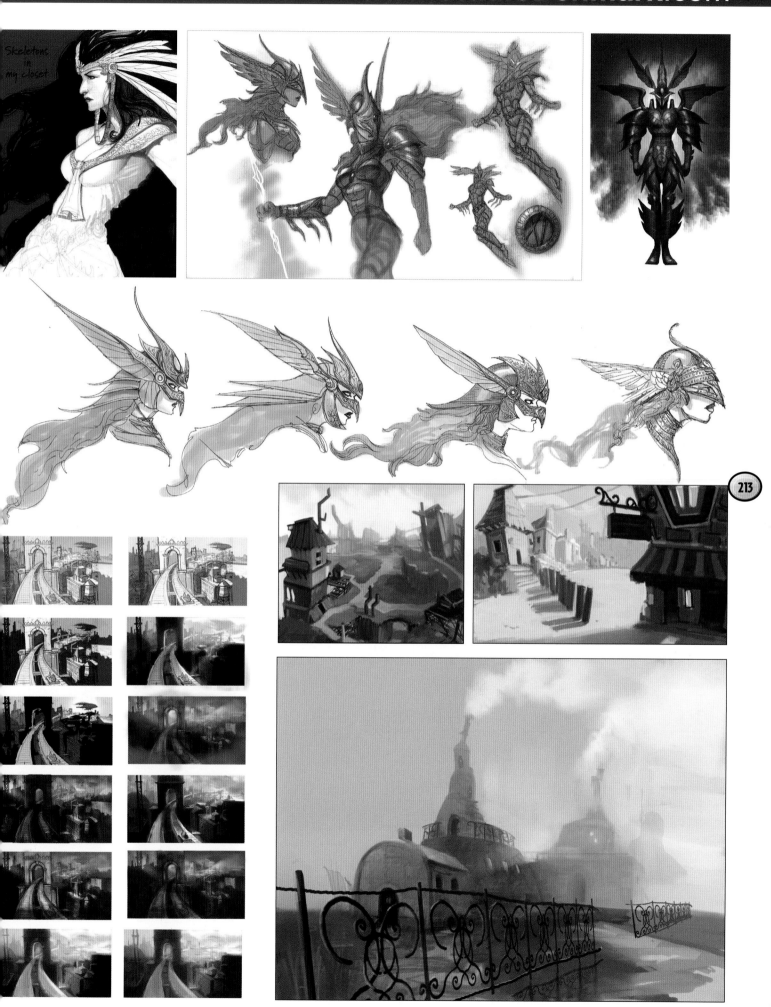

Skeletons in my closet

John Hom

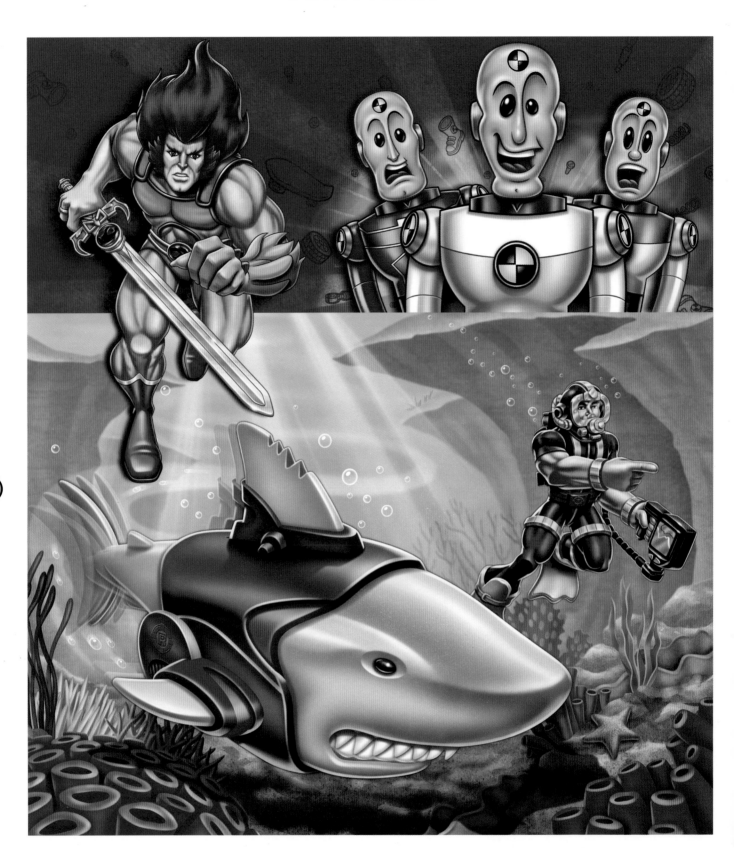

American Artists Reps, Inc.
353 West 53rd Street - Suite 1W
New York, NY 10019
Phone: 212.682.2462
Fax: 212.582.0090
Email: info@aareps.com

Find Your Solution
www.aareps.com

John Hom

215

American Artists Reps, Inc.
353 West 53rd Street - Suite 1W
New York, NY 10019
Phone: 212.682.2462
Fax: 212.582.0090
Email: info@aareps.com

Find Your Solution
www.aareps.com

Garth Glazier

216

American Artists Reps, Inc.
353 West 53rd Street - Suite 1W
New York, NY 10019
Phone: 212.682.2462
Fax: 212.582.0090
Email: info@aareps.com

Find Your Solution
www.aareps.com

Garth Glazier

© 2005 Mattel Inc.

AA REPS

American Artists Reps, Inc.
353 West 53rd Street - Suite 1W
New York, NY 10019
Phone: 212.682.2462
Fax: 212.582.0090
Email: info@aareps.com

Find Your Solution
www.aareps.com

Tony Randazzo

AA REPS

American Artists Reps, Inc.
353 West 53rd Street - Suite 1W
New York, NY 10019
Phone: 212.682.2462
Fax: 212.582.0090
Email: info@aareps.com

Find Your Solution
www.aareps.com

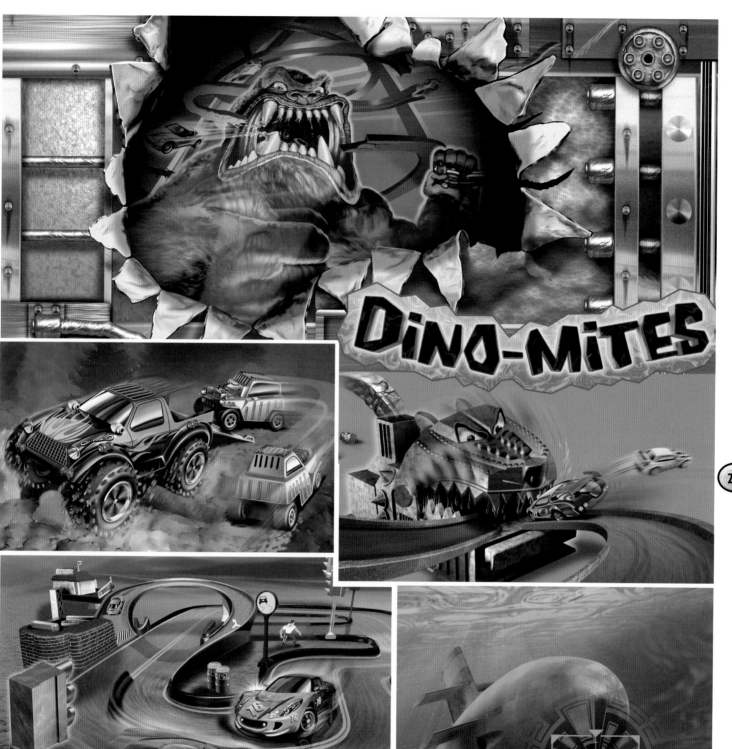

Gary Ciccarelli

220

Stan Watts

John Blackford

American Artists Reps, Inc.
353 West 53rd Street - Suite 1W
New York, NY 10019
Phone: 212.682.2462
Fax: 212.582.0090
Email: info@aareps.com

Find Your Solution
www.aareps.com

221

Jib Hunt

American Artists Reps, Inc.
353 West 53rd Street - Suite 1W
New York, NY 10019
Phone: 212.682.2462
Fax: 212.582.0090
Email: info@aareps.com

Find Your Solution
www.aareps.com

©Marvel

222

Walt Disney CLASSICS
HOME ON THE RANGE

©Disney

Lilo & Stitch's
Island Of Adventures

©Disney

BATCHELLER
626-331-0439
www.keithbatcheller.com
kbatchlr@adelphia.net

©Disney

BATCHELLER
626-331-0439
www.keithbatcheller.com kbatchlr@adelphia.net

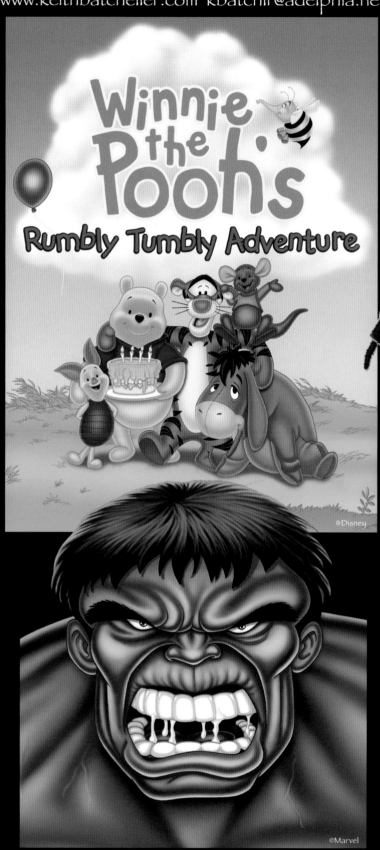

Winnie the Pooh's
Rumbly Tumbly Adventure

©Disney

©Marvel

©Marvel

© Fisher Price

© Fisher Price

223

Karol Kaminski

Clients include The Great American Puzzle Factory,

225

226

SINS OF THE FATHERS

227

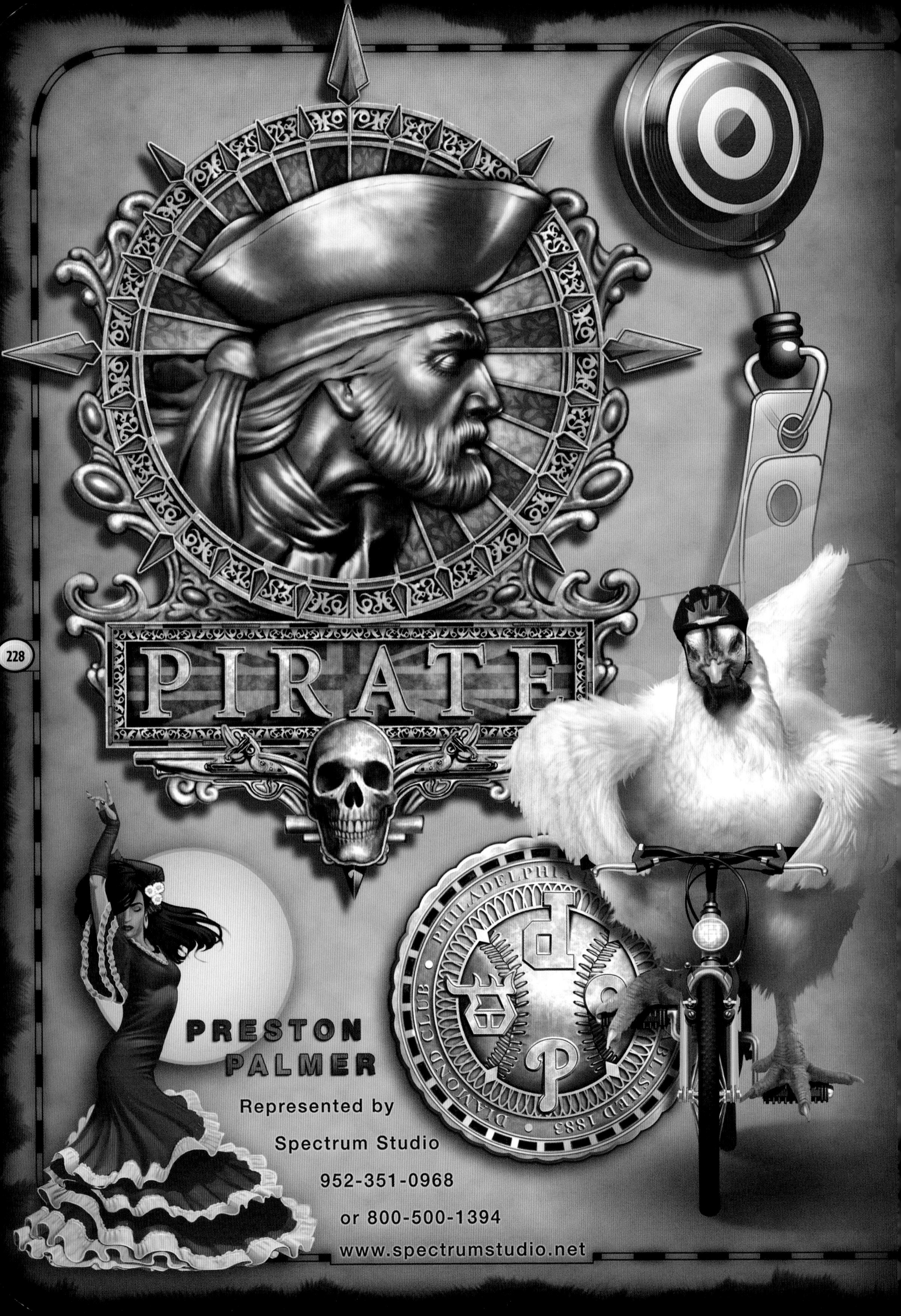
PIRATE
PHILADELPHIA
DIAMOND CLUB
1883
P
PRESTON
PALMER
Represented by
Spectrum Studio
952-351-0968
or 800-500-1394
www.spectrumstudio.net

THE AMAZING MONGO

229

CLOSECOMBAT
FIRST TO FIGHT
• UNITED STATES MARINES •   READY TEAM FIRE ASSIST

3D character model and texture work for PC and Console games.

Elemental Air
(organic concept)

Snow Elemental
(organic concept)

Blacksmith/Armorer-

Air Elemental
(CONCEPTS)

Casino Guard

sed Snake

Blood Elemental (concepts)

230

ILLUSTRATION   STORYBOARDS   CONCEPT DESIGN

POWER-UP
YOUR IDEAS

www.render-ideas.com

A lot of great ideas never see the light of day. Why? Because most people who have them usually lack the means to visually develop them. Prematurely committing to 3D cad models and prototypes often fail to capture the magic of your initial idea. The results are uninspired and disappointing.

IF YOU HAVE AN IDEA WE CAN BRING IT TO LIFE

Our specialty is taking clients abstract – often random – thoughts and visually exploring their possibilities prior to manufacturing models. Through loose concept sketches and finished renderings, **we put you in a confident position to evaluate an idea's viability, see multiple design variations and communicate your thinking to others.**

From Idea...

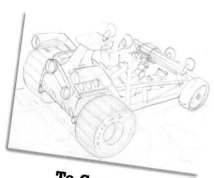

To Concept...

To Rendering

617.566.6710 / www.render-ideas.com

TEPLOW CUCURULLO
COMMUNICATIONS

Julie Heller Rosenfeld

Product & Character Development | Packaging | Design | Illustration

314.574.6958 | julieheller.com | JulieHellerRosenfeld@mac.com

234

237

www.paulsharp.com
studio@paulsharp.com
812-824-3680

239

Search jobs,
post a resume,
and kick start your career!

Gamasutra is the most prominent online resource for game professionals—it's where top companies look for talent, and where professionals find their next jobs.

Search Hundreds of New Job Listings Each Month

Gamasutra's job postings comprise the largest game development job board on the web. Job postings are updated daily—search by company, title, or location.

www.gamasutra.com/jobs

Post Your Resume and Be Discovered

Posting your resume on Gamasutra gets you in front of recruiters from leading companies like Electronic Arts, Sony, and Nintendo. Post your resume today and let these companies come to you!

www.gamasutra.com/resumes

Best of all, these services are free to all registered users.

Don't play games with your career—tap into Gamasutra, the leading online game industry resource

CMP
United Business Media

Gamasutra.com
THE ART & SCIENCE OF MAKING GAMES

Matt Paoletti

Chad Glass / Action Artists

Storyboard Art

241

Jim Wie

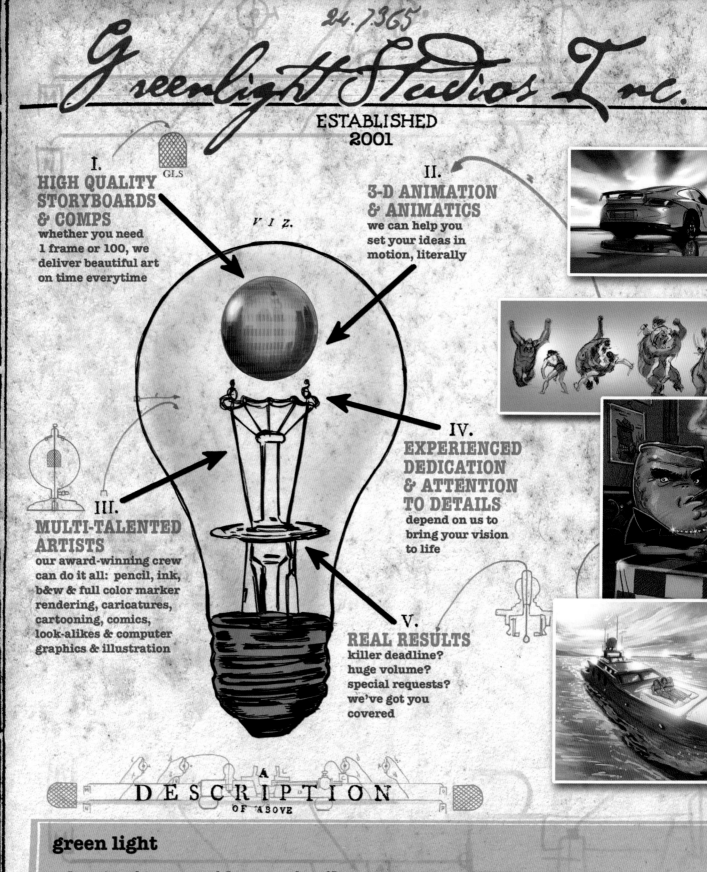

Greenlight Studios Inc.

24.7.365

ESTABLISHED 2001

VIZ.

GLS

I.
HIGH QUALITY STORYBOARDS & COMPS
whether you need 1 frame or 100, we deliver beautiful art on time everytime

II.
3-D ANIMATION & ANIMATICS
we can help you set your ideas in motion, literally

III.
MULTI-TALENTED ARTISTS
our award-winning crew can do it all: pencil, ink, b&w & full color marker rendering, caricatures, cartooning, comics, look-alikes & computer graphics & illustration

IV.
EXPERIENCED DEDICATION & ATTENTION TO DETAILS
depend on us to bring your vision to life

V.
REAL RESULTS
killer deadline? huge volume? special requests? we've got you covered

A DESCRIPTION
OF ABOVE

green light

n **1**: a signal to proceed [syn: go-ahead]
2: permission to proceed with a project or to take action
3: the premier art studio specializing in providing the very best storyboards, shooting boards, comp art, animatics, 3-d rendering and animation for the advertising, television and film industries

649 east 14th street
suite 2d
new york, ny
10009

www.greenlightstudiosinc.com

e-mail:
info@greenlightstudiosinc.com
bj@greenlightstudiosinc.com

phone: 212.614.2434
973.509.5355
fax: 212.614.2435
cell: 917.855.2417

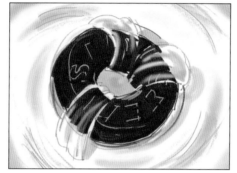

GO animatic.com ➤

we'll move you

416 785 3387

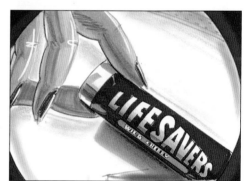

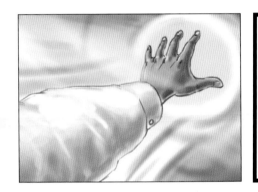

245

WIZ
STORY BOARD GUY!
312 338 6474
jimwiz@ameritech.net

247

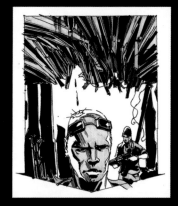

CHAD GLASS
CRAIG CARTWRIGHT
MICAH COSTANZA
RAYMOND CONSING
RUSTY DUMAS
RYAN FALKNER
VINCENT LUCIDO

248

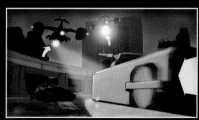

MATT **PAOLETTI**